INTERACTIVE GUIDE

THE
BAIT
OF
SATAN

INTERACTIVE GUIDE

THE BAIT OF SATAN

JOHN BEVERE

Group questions and devotions:

Vincent M. Newfield, senior writer and editor • Victoria A. Newfield, assistant writer and editor

Printed in the United States of America

SPECIAL MARKET SALES
Organizations, churches, pastors, and small group leaders can receive special discounts when purchasing this book and other resources from John Bevere. For information, please call 1-800-648-1477 or visit www.MessengerInternational.org.

Contents

About This Interactive Guide

Welcome to *The Bait of Satan Interactive Guide!* We believe God has ordered your steps and strategically placed this learning opportunity before you at this time in your life. You can complete this study individually or in a group setting. While it has been designed to be used over the course of six weeks, feel free to adjust it to your needs.

Each chapter of this guide corresponds with the six video sessions and includes:

- An *Overview* to help you get started and make the most of each session
- *Discussion Questions* for individual or group reflection
- An *Activity* to help you (and those participating) personally apply what you're learning
- A *Session Summary* to encapsulate and help you remember the main takeaways from each session
- *Daily Devotions* that include personal questions, Scripture to meditate on, and suggested action steps to make the truths your own
- A *Journal* space to write personal insights the Holy Spirit shows you throughout each week

If you're using this guide as part of *The Bait of Satan* six-week study, we recommend that you read the overview for each week, watch or listen to the teaching session, and answer the discussion questions. Then read the corresponding book chapters, which are listed after each Session Summary, and complete the daily devotions for that chapter over the course of the week.

We pray that God's Spirit will help you identify the condition of your heart, align with His Word regarding the sin of offense, release any offenses you may be holding, and begin to experience healing and reconciliation with others. By His grace, may you be empowered to live free from the trap of offense!

Enjoy!

"As I travel around the world ministering, I have been able to observe one of the enemy's most deadly and deceptive traps. It imprisons countless Christians, severs relationships, and widens the existing breaches between us. It is the trap of offense."

—JOHN BEVERE

CHAPTER 1

Massive Offense

OVERVIEW

- **Get Started:** Welcome participants and ask them to ponder this question: "What is one of the most life-defining moments in your life—a time you learned a lesson or made a decision that greatly affected you?" Allow a few participants to briefly share their memories. Communicate to the group that the study they're about to begin will likely be a new, life-defining moment. Encourage them to be sincerely open and ready to hear and act on God's leading.

- **Pray:** In this foundational session, it's vital for everyone to be open to the voice of the Holy Spirit and allow Him to reveal any offenses they may be holding on to. Pray that He enables them to identify and surrender any unforgiveness in their hearts to Him, so that the process of healing can begin.

- **Watch:** View Session 1 of *The Bait of Satan Study* together.

- **Discuss:** Ask the group, "What is your gut reaction to the teaching you just heard? What parts challenged you most?"

After hearing their responses, you can spark further conversation by using the discussion questions found in this chapter.

- **Read:** This week we recommend that you read chapters 1-2 in *The Bait of Satan* book.

- **Devotions**: This week's devotions focus on the condition of our hearts, our expectations, dealing with wrong thinking, and pursuing oneness. Encourage the group to invest just a few minutes daily to carefully read through each one, answering the questions honestly.

- **Journal**: Take time to jot down personal thoughts and feelings while watching the teaching, participating in group discussions, and walking through the daily devotions. Anything the Holy Spirit brings to life is priceless and worth writing down.

GROUP DISCUSSION QUESTIONS

1. Jesus said, "If your brother sins against you . . . seven times in a day, and seven times in a day returns to you, saying, 'I repent,' you shall forgive him" (Luke 17:3-4). What *repeated offenses* do you find hardest to forgive? Why do you think this is the case?

2. When we're hurt and/or offended, we usually begin to *build walls* to protect ourselves from further pain—often without even thinking. Describe some of the barriers we set up in our relationships to guard and insulate ourselves from additional heartache.

3. Offense often comes indirectly as a result of *unmet expectations*—we expect someone to say a certain thing or act a certain way, and when they don't, we get offended. How do you normally react when you're disappointed by someone's actions? What do you think is a healthy, godly way to respond?

4. Have you ever become immediately suspicious or frustrated when someone unexpectedly did or said something kind to you? Maybe you questioned their motives or even became irritated by their actions? Why do you think we sometimes respond this way?

5. When our hearts are free of offense and filled with God's love, we're willing to give to others without expecting anything in return. On the other hand, if we're offended, we seek to preserve and protect ourselves. The longer we hold on to offense, the more inward our focus becomes. Describe what this inward, self-focus looks like. Why is it so dangerous to us individually and as the Body of Christ?

(Consider reading James 3:15-16 as a group.)

ACTIVITY

When a person gets sick, he or she often goes to the doctor to find out what's wrong. In order to properly diagnose and treat the sickness, the doctor asks them to describe all of the symptoms he or she is experiencing. Get together with two or more people (or you can do this by yourself) and write down as many symptoms of offense that you can think of.

Make the top part of your list the "early warning signs" a person would feel and the bottom of your list the symptoms they would experience after allowing offense to fester in their heart for months, years, or even decades. This activity will help open your heart and mind to the searchlight of God's Spirit and prepare you for the upcoming devotions.

SESSION SUMMARY

The word *offense* is the Greek word *skandalon*, which is the part (or trigger) of a hunter's trap that holds the bait. When we take the bait of offense, we trigger the enemy's trap and (knowingly or unknowingly) become captive to his will.

The people who can hurt us most are those closest to us. The greater our expectations, the greater potential we have to be offended.

Once we're offended, we begin to build walls in our relationships to protect and insulate ourselves from additional wounds. Over time, these walls become mental and emotional strongholds that do us more harm than good.

Holding on to offense activates a progressive chain of pain in our lives. Offense leads to *betrayal*, betrayal turns into *hatred*, hatred gives way to *deception*, and deception opens the door to *lawlessness*.

O In these last days before Christ's return, offense will become widespread, specifically among believers. We must be on guard and careful not to fall into this deadly trap.

DAY 1
Examine Your Heart

...For you, the righteous God, look deep within the hearts of men and examine all their motives and their thoughts.
—PSALM 7:9 TLB

The condition of our heart is vital to our overall health—both physically and spiritually. When we've been hurt and have not released the offense, we've put our lives in danger by taking the bait. The scary part is, many times we're not even aware of it. Thank God He doesn't leave us there:

"But I, God, search the heart and examine the mind. I get to the heart of the human. I get to the root of things. I treat them as they really are, not as they pretend to be."—JEREMIAH 17:10 MSG

How does He do this for us? We are clearly told:

"For the Word that God speaks is alive and full of power [making it active, operative, energizing, and effective]; it is sharper than any two-edged sword, penetrating to the dividing line of the breath of life (soul) and [the immortal] spirit...exposing *and* sifting *and* analyzing *and* judging the very thoughts and purposes of the heart."—HEBREWS 4:12 AMP

While we, in ourselves, are clueless about what's going on inside us, God is not. He has the amazing ability to cut straight to our heart. He can go where no man can go and see what no man can see. And He still loves us! What an amazing God we serve!

Take a few moments to pray and chew on this prayer David penned:

> "Search me, O God, and know my heart; test me and know my anxious thoughts. Point out anything in me that offends you, and lead me along the path of everlasting life."—PSALM 139:23-24 NLT

Ask God, "Is there any offense in my heart? Am I holding on to unforgiveness toward someone who has hurt or disappointed me? Please show me, Lord. In Jesus's name, Amen." Be still and listen. What is God revealing to you? Write down any names and situations that come to mind.

_____

_____

_____

_____

_____

_____

To help you answer this question honestly, refer to the list
of symptoms written down during the Activity.

Take a moment now and *release* these people and situations to the Lord. Ask Him to forgive you for holding on to offense and invite Him into your heart and circumstances. What He reveals, He will heal as you let Him into your life. Jot down anything else God is speaking to you.

DAY 2
Adjust Your Expectations

Make allowance for each other's faults, and forgive anyone who offends you. Remember, the Lord forgave you, so you must forgive others.
—Colossians 3:13 NLT

Jesus said, "It is impossible that no offenses should come..." (Luke 17:1). In other words, if we're breathing, we're going to have opportunities to be offended. People will say and do things that hurt—it's just a part of life.

Our greatest potential to be offended is with people close to us—our spouse, children, siblings, parents, coworkers, fellow church members, our pastors, and even God Himself. We tend to expect the most from those we love deepest. When our expectations aren't met, disappointment sets in, which quickly turns into offense if it isn't dealt with properly.

Stop and think: *Am I truly at peace with those closest to me? Or is there someone I'm having a really hard time liking—much less loving?* Who is the Holy Spirit bringing to mind?

_____

_____

_____

_____

_____

What specifically are they doing (or *not* doing) that is offensive to you?

_____

_____

_____

_____

What are some of your *expectations* of them?

_____

_____

_____

Are these expectations realistic? Are they demanding? If they are realistic but aren't being met, ask God to give you *His* perspective of you, them, and the situation (write what He reveals).

_____

_____

_____

_____

Live creatively, friends. If someone falls into sin, forgivingly restore him, saving your critical comments for yourself. You might be needing forgiveness before the day's out (MSG). Help carry each other's burdens. In this way you will follow Christ's teachings (GW).—GALATIANS 6:1-2

DAY 3
Demolish Strongholds

*I use God's mighty weapons, not those made by men, to
knock down the devil's strongholds. These weapons can
break down every proud argument against God and every
wall that can be built to keep men from finding Him....*

—2 CORINTHIANS 10:4-5 TLB

None of us like to be hurt. Typically, we will avoid pain whenever
possible. So when someone offends us, we often begin a subconscious
building program, erecting walls in our relationships to protect ourselves. God identifies these walls as *strongholds*—set patterns of rea-
soning (thinking) through which we process (or filter) information.

The word *stronghold* in 2 Corinthians 10:4 is the Greek word *ochu-
roma*. It was a term used to describe a *castle* or *fortress* that had very
thick, impenetrable walls built to keep intruders out. Interestingly, the
same word for stronghold here was also used to describe a *prison*—a
place of punishment and torment.[1] Are you getting a glimpse of what
strongholds do in your life?

David Wilkerson, noted author, pastor, and prophet to America
for over four decades, explains:

"A **stronghold** is an accusation planted firmly in your mind.
Satan establishes strongholds in God's people by implanting in
their minds lies, falsehoods and misconceptions .... The devil
may try to convince you that you have a right to hold onto bitterness because you've been wronged. He'll try to destroy your
marriage by persuading you, 'You can't endure this relationship

any longer unless your spouse changes.' If you keep listening to his lies, you'll begin to believe them after a while."[2]

Think about it. What **walls** have you built to protect yourself from being hurt again? What specific types of thinking regarding your relationships is God reminding you of?

_____

_____

_____

_____

What is the cure for destructive strongholds? Seek God! ". . . His name is the Lord. He _destroys strongholds_ and ruins fortresses" (Amos 5:8-9 GW).

As you recognize the enemy's lies and repent to God for believing them (see 1 John 1:9), He will forgive you and tear down the stronghold of offense in your soul. Then, dig into His Word and begin to replace the enemy's lies with truth.

How powerful is God's Word in _your_ life? Take a moment to meditate on these passages: **Hebrews 4:12; James 1:21;** and **Jeremiah 23:28-29.** What's God showing you in these verses that you can apply in your life?

_____

_____

_____

_____

DAY 4
Break the Chain Reaction

Great peace have they who love Your law; nothing
shall offend them or make them stumble.
—Psalm 119:165 AMP

Holding on to offense and not dealing with it properly results in a
tragic *chain of pain* in our lives and the lives of those around us. Carefully read Jesus's words in Matthew 24:10-12:

"And then many will be offended, will betray one another, and
will hate one another. Then many false prophets will rise up and
deceive many. And because lawlessness will abound, the love of
many will grow cold."

How many *links* in the chain of pain can you identify in this passage?

_____

_____

_____

In your own words, explain what each of these are and how they're
connected.

_____

_____

_____

When we're offended, self-preservation becomes our focus, making us a prime candidate for betrayal. To *betray* someone is to seek what benefits us at their expense. Take a moment to ask God, "Have I done this? Has the love in my heart grown cold in any of my relationships? Am I on the verge of betrayal?" Listen. What is God showing you?

_____

_____

_____

_____

Lawlessness is an end product of offense. It's the Greek word *anomia*, which essentially means "contempt for and disobedience to the law (God's Word)." Again, pause and pray, "Lord, am I ignoring what Your Word says regarding certain areas of my life? Do I have contempt or disrespect for truth?" Be still and listen. What's the Holy Spirit speaking?

_____

_____

_____

_____

In light of your answers and the principles you're hearing in this teaching, what actions do you feel God is asking you to take?

_____

_____

_____

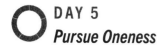

DAY 5
Pursue Oneness

*Make it your aim to be at **one** in the Spirit, and you
will inevitably be at peace with one another.*
—Ephesians 4:3 Phillips

Jesus said that in the last days before His return, many who once believed in Him would become offended and abandon their faith. "And the love of the great body of people will grow cold . . ." (Matthew 24:12 AMP). He warns us of this so we can avoid falling prey to it.

Watchman Nee, a very insightful and devoted Christian leader and author who served in China and was imprisoned for his faith, aptly stated:

"The work of God is to make us *one* body, but the work of Satan
is to cause us to be torn asunder. Satan uses our corrupted flesh,
our stubborn self, and the world which we covet to carry out
his work of destruction. . . . If these elements are permitted to
remain in our lives, we clearly make room for Satan to work his
work of disintegration."[3]

How can we effectively combat Satan's strategy of disintegration? By pursuing oneness. Watchman Nee continues:

"Oneness is when God has His absolute place in us. Oneness is
when He alone is in all, when He fills all. When the children of
God are filled with God, they harmonize with each other."[4]

What does pursuing oneness look like in God's eyes? Take time to meditate on these passages:

"This is what I have asked of God for you: that you will be encouraged and knit together by strong ties of love, and that you will have the rich experience of knowing Christ with real certainty and clear understanding . . . ."—COLOSSIANS 2:2 TLB

"Make allowance for each other's faults, and forgive anyone who offends you. Remember, the Lord forgave you, so you must forgive others. Above all, clothe yourselves with love, which binds us all together in perfect harmony."
—COLOSSIANS 3:13-14 NLT

". . . We will speak the truth in love, growing in every way more and more like Christ, who is the head of His body, the church. He makes the whole body fit together perfectly. As each part does its own special work, it helps the other parts grow, so that the whole body is healthy and growing and full of love."
—EPHESIANS 4:15-16 NLT

". . . Make me truly happy by loving each other and agreeing wholeheartedly with each other, working together with one heart and mind and purpose. Don't be selfish; don't live to make a good impression on others. Be humble, thinking of others as better than yourself. Don't just think about your own affairs, but be interested in others, too, and in what they are doing."—PHILIPPIANS 2:2-4 TLB

What qualities of oneness is God showing you that you can cultivate and put into practice?

_____

_____

_____

_____

_____

_____

_____

_____

FOOD FOR THOUGHT . . .

Our enemy's plan to trap and control us is triggered when we pick up an offense. Offenses left unchecked will eventually separate us from God and others and open doors for the enemy to forge a chain of pain in our lives. Seize this moment to be gut-level honest with yourself and God about past and present hurts.

Have you taken up offense with someone in your family, workplace, or church? What walls have become strongholds in your soul? Take time to pray and ask God to guide you into the truth about yourself and the situations you're facing. Pour your heart out on paper, capturing the insight He gives you.

JOURNAL

_____

_____

_____

_____

_____

_____

_____

_____

_____

_____

_____

_____

_____

_____

_____

_____

(1) Rick Renner, adapted from *Sparkling Gems from the Greek* (Tulsa, OK: Teach All Nations, 2003) pp. 918-919. (2) David Wilkerson, *The New Covenant Unveiled* (Lindale, TX: Wilkerson Trust Publications, 2000) p. 115. (3) Watchman Nee, *The Body of Christ: A Reality* (New York, Christian Fellowship Publishers, Inc., 1978) p. 47. (4) Ibid., p. 48.

"If you stay free from offense you will stay in God's will. If you become offended you will be taken captive by the enemy to fulfill his own purpose and will. Take your pick. It is much more beneficial to stay free from offense."

—JOHN BEVERE

CHAPTER 2

How Could This Happen to Me?

OVERVIEW

- **Get Started:** Take some time to welcome participants and pose this question: "Can you remember a time in your life when you said, 'How could this happen to me?' If so, what was going on?" Allow a few people to share their experiences. Convey to the group that Session 2 focuses on someone who *lived* this question—a man named Joseph. Encourage them to listen for similarities between his story and theirs.

- **Pray:** Everyone in the group has gone and will go through mistreatment, which means it's vital that they're prepared to handle it correctly so it doesn't dominate their destiny. Ask the Holy Spirit to give each participant grace not to give up or become offended and bitter with God and others; that they can see the *big picture* of their lives—to know that what they're going through has both a purpose and definite end to it.

- **Watch:** View **Session 2** of *The Bait of Satan Study* together.

- **Discuss**: What we focus on we empower. Tell the group, "Don't think about pink elephants. Push any images of Dumbo out of your mind. You can fix your thoughts on anything. Just don't imagine any large, tough-skinned pachyderms." Pause briefly, and then ask, "What happened? What were you focused on? What does this say to you about your thoughts and your words about the person who hurt you?" Allow people to weigh in and then dive in to the discussion questions for Chapter 2.

- **Read:** This week we recommend that you read chapter 3 in *The Bait of Satan* book.

- **Devotions**: This week's devotions center on trusting God in the middle of mistreatment, believing He's present in our difficulties, cooperating with His correction, and holding tightly to our dreams. Once again, ask the group to invest a few minutes daily to carefully read through each one and answer the questions honestly.

- **Journal**: Nothing surpasses the power of handwritten notes to boost our memory. The Holy Spirit is going to reveal truth as you journey through this study. Challenge everyone to write what He speaks. Scriptures, principles, and personal insights that stand out are important to write down while they are fresh in our minds. You'll never regret investing the time.

GROUP DISCUSSION QUESTIONS

Joseph was a man who loved God deeply and had a significant call on his life. He was loyal to his father, Jacob, and highly favored by him.

Out of extreme jealousy, Joseph's older brothers sold him into slavery, which began fourteen years of intense difficulties.

1. Do you think Joseph had to work through any feelings of anger, hatred, bitterness, or revenge? Why or why not? What other emotions have *you* had to work through as a result of being mistreated?

2. In what ways can you personally identify with Joseph's story? How does his response and how he was rewarded give you hope and encouragement?

3. Jesus also suffered greatly. Why? Scripture says, "Even though Jesus was God's Son, He learned obedience from the things He suffered. In this way, God qualified Him as a perfect High Priest, and He became the source of eternal salvation for all those who obey Him" (Hebrews 5:8-9 NLT). What do the examples from Jesus's and Joseph's lives speak to you about the purpose of your hardships?

   (Consider checking out James 1:2-4 as a group.)

4. Look back over your life. Recall a situation in which you were hurt or mistreated in what seemed like the worst possible way. Can you see something *positive* about it now that you couldn't see then? How did God prepare you back then for where you are now? Using what you learned, share some words of encouragement with those around you who may be going through a similar difficulty.

5. Both Joseph and Jesus endured severe suffering. How do you think they endured the bitterest kind of pain? What wisdom can you gather from their lives to help you endure your difficulties? Consider these passages:

> Keep your eyes on Jesus, who both began and finished this race we're in. Study how He did it. Because He never lost sight of where He was headed—that exhilarating finish in and with God—He could put up with anything along the way: Cross, shame, whatever. And now He's there, in the place of honor, right alongside God. When you find yourselves flagging in your faith, go over that story again, item by item, that long litany of hostility He plowed through. That will shoot adrenaline into your souls!—HEBREWS 12:2-3 MSG

> So we're not giving up. How could we! Even though on the outside it often looks like things are falling apart on us, on the inside, where God is making new life, not a day goes by without His unfolding grace. These hard times are small potatoes compared to the coming good times, the lavish celebration prepared for us. There's far more here than meets the eye. The things we see now are here today, gone tomorrow. But the things we can't see now will last forever.
> —2 CORINTHIANS 4:16-18 MSG

(Also consider checking out Ephesians 1:18-23 as a group.)

A major sign that a person is offended is *pointing a finger of blame* at others, whether the recipient has actually done anything or not. Get together with one or more people and take turns interviewing each other (or you can do this by yourself). Ask the following questions and write your answers:

- Have you ever been on the receiving end of an untrue accusation or blamed for something you didn't do? How did you feel? How did you handle it?
- Were you able to resolve the issue and make peace with the other person?
- Identify two or three things you learned from the situation that taught you to be cautious about pinning blame on someone too quickly.

SESSION SUMMARY

All of us will experience mistreatment in this life. When it happens, we have two options: give in to the temptation to blame others and complain to God, or let go of the offense and leave it in God's hands. If we choose to trust Him and not to be offended, we'll come out of it better, not bitter.

No human on earth and no devil out of hell can ever take you out of God's will! He holds your destiny securely in His hands. The only one who can take you out of His will is *you.*

○ Our heavenly Father is never surprised, shocked, or shaken by what we go through. His plans for us are solidified—not shattered—by the enemy's schemes.

○ God has already laid out the master plan for our lives. Before Earth's foundation, He chose us as His secret weapon for this time. He has a specific life mission for each of us to complete, but training always comes before a mission.

○ Often, what looks like an abortion of God's plan can actually be the road to its fulfillment—if we stay obedient to Him and free of offense.

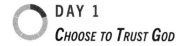

DAY 1
CHOOSE TO TRUST GOD

Trust the Lord completely; don't ever trust yourself.
In everything you do, put God first, and He will
direct you and crown your efforts with success.
—PROVERBS 3:5-6 TLB

Have you ever played "The Blame Game"? Sadly, we all have. It's a terrible tendency each of us can fall into when things don't turn out the way we planned. Adam and Eve were the first to play it, and it's possible Joseph played it while he was in prison. Maybe he wrestled with thoughts like, *If it weren't for my brothers, I could be home right now, enjoying a great life with my father.*

Have you ever thought like that? How would you fill in the blanks to complete this sentence?

"If it weren't for _____, I'd have a better _____ (job, marriage, family, self-image, social life, bank account, or something else you want but don't have)."

What long-term effects will likely result from a mindset of blaming others?

_____

_____

_____

_____

To help you see and understand the effects of blaming,
refer to the questions you answered in the Activity.

What healthy shift in perspective would serve you better?

_____

_____

_____

For help, check out **Psalm 34:9-10; 37:1-9; Proverbs 3:5-8; Isaiah 26:3-4;** and **Jeremiah 17:7-8**.

> Do all things without grumbling and faultfinding and com-
> plaining [against God] and questioning and doubting [among
> yourselves], that you may show yourselves to be blameless and
> guileless, innocent and uncontaminated, children of God with-
> out blemish . . . .—PHILIPPIANS 2:14-15 AMP

The people of Israel, whom God had miraculously delivered out of
Egyptian bondage, were frequently offended with Moses and God
because of their hardships. They constantly blamed them and com-
plained about the circumstances they were experiencing.

What happened because they refused to deal with and let go of
their offenses?

_____

_____

_____

Check out Numbers **14:20-35; Psalm 95:8-11;** and **Hebrews 3:16-19**. What can you personally learn from this example and apply to *your* life?

_____

_____

_____

_____

_____

DAY 2
STAY THE COURSE

*God, teach me lessons for living so I can stay the
course. Give me insight so I can do what You tell me—
my whole life one long, obedient response.*
—PSALM 119:33-34 MSG

God's Word says, "Many evils confront the [consistently] righteous,
but the Lord delivers him out of them all" (Psalm 34:19 AMP). Our
lives are held securely in His hands, and *no one* is able to snatch us
away from Him (see John 10:28-29).

The only one who can take you out of God's will is *you*. How? One
major way is through holding on to offense. The longer we choose not
to forgive, the more resentful and bitter we become. The more bitter
we are, the more vulnerable we become to the temptation to get even.

Carefully read **Romans 12:17-20; 1 Peter 3:8-9;** and **Hebrews
10:30-31** and explain what God says about getting revenge.

_____

_____

_____

_____

_____

_____

_____

If you take matters into your own hands, what will *not* happen—what will you hinder?

_____

_____

_____

_____

_____

With His strength, how does God want you to respond to the people who hurt you?

_____

_____

_____

_____

_____

"Everything can be taken from a man but one thing: the last of human freedoms—to choose one's attitude in any given set of circumstances."—VICTOR FRANKL[1]

Joseph stayed the course! He chose not to harbor hatred or take revenge on his brothers, and he was rewarded. What's God's promise to *you* for staying the course? Read **Galatians 6:9; James 1:12; 1 Peter**

5:6, 10; and **Mark 10:29-30.** What's the Holy Spirit showing you in these passages?

_____

_____

_____

_____

_____

_____

. . . Trust the Lord; and remember that other Christians all around the world are going through these sufferings too. After you have suffered a little while, our God, who is full of kindness through Christ, will give you His eternal glory. He personally will come and pick you up, and set you firmly in place, and make you stronger than ever.—1 PETER 5:9-10 TLB

DAY 3
BELIEVE GOD IS PRESENT

God doesn't miss a thing—He's alert to good and evil alike.
—PROVERBS 15:3 MSG

When we go through dark, difficult times, it's encouraging to know that God is with us. He's promised to *never* leave us. Nothing in our lives comes as a surprise or shock to Him.

Many people, both Christian and non-Christian alike, ask questions about God. Here are three common ones. Carefully read the Scriptures for the answers and write what the Lord shows you.

Question: "Is God *involved* in my life?"
God ANSWERS: Psalm 37:23; Proverbs 16:9; 20:24; and Hebrews 13:5-6

_____

_____

_____

Question: "Is God *aware* and does He *care* about what concerns me?"
God ANSWERS: Psalm 139:17-18; Isaiah 49:15-16; Matthew 6:25-34; and 1 Peter 5:7

_____

_____

_____

Question: "Does God *love* me and have a *good plan* for my life?" God ANSWERS: 1 John 3:1; Isaiah 54:10; Jeremiah 29:11; and Psalm 40:1-5

_____

_____

_____

_____

_____

_____

King David ruled Israel for forty years and lived about 1,000 years before Christ. Through many highs and lows of life, he was moved by the Holy Spirit to declare:

> "O Lord, you have examined my heart and know everything about me. You know when I sit down or stand up. You know my thoughts even when I'm far away. You see me when I travel and when I rest at home. You know everything I do. You know what I am going to say even before I say it, LORD. You go before me and follow me. You place Your hand of blessing on my head. Such knowledge is too wonderful for me, too great for me to understand!
>
> "You made all the delicate, inner parts of my body and knit me together in my mother's womb. Thank you for making me so wonderfully complex! Your workmanship is marvelous—how well I know it. You watched me as I was being formed in utter

seclusion, as I was woven together in the dark of the womb. You saw me before I was born. Every day of my life was recorded in Your book. Every moment was laid out before a single day had passed."—PSALM 139:1-6, 13-16 NLT

Slowly reread this eye-opening passage. What aspects of your life is God aware of? How do these verses breathe new life and hope into you?

_____

_____

_____

_____

_____

_____

DAY 4
Cooperate with God's Refinement

...God's correction is always right
and for our best good,
that we may share His holiness.

—HEBREWS 12:10 TLB

God, our heavenly Father, loves us beyond description and wants the absolute best for our lives. So like every good dad, He brings us correction when we need it. In Scripture, correction is sometimes described as troubles, trials, tribulation, hardships, and discipline. Regardless of the name, God has one primary goal in mind—to refine us.

Charles Stanley, seasoned pastor and insightful teacher of over forty-five years, has experienced his share of God's correction. *Adversity*, as he describes it ...

"... is not simply a tool. It is God's most effective tool for the advancement of our spiritual lives. The circumstances and events that we see as setbacks are oftentimes the very things that launch us into periods of intense spiritual growth. Once we begin to understand this, and accept it as a spiritual fact of life, adversity becomes easier to bear."[2]

Are you enduring a difficult time in your life right now? It could be that God is correcting your course to ensure you reach the destination He's planned. Take a moment to describe the season of life you're in.

_____

_____

_____

One question often plagues us when we suffer: "Did I do something wrong to deserve this?" Keep in mind Jesus suffered, but *never* sinned. Read and ponder the description of His rejection and suffering in Isaiah 53:2-5. What reason(s) for suffering is God showing you from His example?

_____

_____

_____

_____

Also check out Joseph's response to his brothers after he had suffered in slavery and imprisonment (see Genesis 45:4-8).

What is God's *purpose* in discipline, and what *blessings* can you expect when you surrender to it? Carefully read **Hebrews 12:5-11** and **1 Peter 1:6-7** and write what the Holy Spirit shows you.

_____

_____

_____

Consider also Zechariah 13:9 and Malachi 3:1-3.

... Exercise daily in God—no spiritual flabbiness, please! Workouts in the gymnasium are useful, but a disciplined life in God is far more so, making you fit both today and forever.—1 TIMOTHY 4:7-8 MSG

DAY 5
Hold Tightly to Your Dream

Let us hold tightly without wavering to the hope we
affirm, for God can be trusted to keep His promise.
—Hebrews 10:23 nlt

Joseph had a dream, but it took over twenty years for it to become a reality. In the middle of all his struggles and pain, he didn't know the end of his story any more than we know ours.

What's *your* dream? What ideas and desires has God planted in your heart? How can you harness your gifts and talents to bring the life and love of Jesus to your world? Take time to write it.

_____

_____

_____

_____

_____

_____

Then the Lord answered me, "Write the vision. Make it clear on tablets so that anyone can read it quickly. The vision will still happen at the appointed time. It hurries toward its goal. It won't be a lie. If it's delayed, wait for it. It will certainly happen. It won't be late.—Habakkuk 2:2-3 gw

Carefully read **Habakkuk 2:2-3** above, along with **Numbers 23:19** and **1 Kings 8:56**. What does God remind us of again and again? How do these promises encourage you?

_____

_____

_____

_____

David Jeremiah has served as a pastor, author, and teacher on radio and television. As a survivor of two bouts with cancer, he shares the candid details of his journey in his book *When Your Life Falls Apart*. Here's a bit of his insight on God's timing:

> "The same God who has been there for you in the past is the God who is going to be there for you in the future. He will bring resolution in His own time, according to His own purposes. We become preoccupied with our circumstances; God is preoccupied with our *character*. He will allow the tough times for the higher good of our character until He is finished with the great work that is invisible to our earthly eyes."[3]

Indeed, character is crucial in God's eyes. That's what was forming in Joseph through all the twists and turns of trouble he faced. How can we tell that he was truly *free* of offense when his dream finally came true? Carefully read how he treated his brothers when he revealed his true identity (Genesis 45:1-15) and after their father died (Genesis 50:15-21). What did he *not* do that he certainly could've done? What did he give his brothers that they didn't deserve? What does his example show you about your own character?

_____

_____

_____

_____

_____

_____

_____

_____

FOOD FOR THOUGHT . . .

Mistreatment always brings us to a crossroads. One trail is paved with blaming and complaining. The other is marked by trusting God and leaving offenses in His hands. When we choose to let go and believe God has our back, we grow better—not bitter—and stay on the path of our divine destiny.

Use this fork in the road to consider what offenses you've encountered on the way here. Which route would you have taken *before* you began this study? How about now? Take this moment and ask God to open your eyes to the truth about your past and present struggles. Pour your heart out on paper, capturing the insight He gives you.

JOURNAL

_____

_____

_____

_____

_____

_____

_____

_____

_____

_____

_____

_____

_____

_____

_____

_____

_____

_____

_____

_____

"David was rejected by the one who should have fathered him, yet he remained loyal even after Saul's death. It is easy to be loyal to a leader or father who loves you, but what about one who is out to destroy you? Will you be a man or woman after the heart of God, or will you seek to avenge yourself?"

—JOHN BEVERE

CHAPTER 3

My Father, My Father!

- **Get Started:** Greet the group members and present this question: "Have you experienced rejection from an esteemed leader in your life? If so, how would you describe your relationship with them, both before and after?" Allow a few people to share their stories. Let everyone know that Session 3 focuses on a man who had one of the worst-case rejection scenarios—David, who ran from Saul for nearly fifteen years. Encourage them to listen for David's reaction to Saul's insanity.

- **Pray:** The temptation to get even is one we all have and will face. Many times it seems perfectly justified—just as it did in David's case. But it is the furthest thing from what God wants for us. Ask the Holy Spirit to soften the hearts of each participant to leave revenge to the ultimate Avenger. As they do, they will remain open to His plans and blessings.

- **Watch:** View **Session 3** of *The Bait of Satan Study* together.

- **Discuss**: Pose this question to the group: "Have you ever said or thought these words: 'Desperate times call for desperate measures' or 'You just don't know what he's done to me!'? Have you ever used this kind of thinking as an excuse to trash-talk someone in authority who had it out for you? If so, what drove you to it?" Listen and use the group's responses as a springboard to dive into the Chapter 3 discussion questions.

- **Read:** This week we recommend that you read chapters 4-6 in *The Bait of Satan* book.

- **Devotions**: This week's devotions focus on fearing the Lord, cultivating godly character, honoring our leaders, and abiding in God's love. Once again, ask the group to invest a few minutes daily to carefully read through each devotion and answer the questions honestly.

- **Journal**: God is going to bring things to the surface as people participate in this week's study. He's going to reveal things about Himself and His Word and point out reasons why we act and react the way we do. Once again, encourage people to note these eye-opening insights in the Journal section.

GROUP DISCUSSION QUESTIONS

1. David was a man after God's own heart, yet God placed him under the corrupt authority of King Saul. Are there any *Davids* in your life that you're discounting or devaluing because

of a *Saul* they once served? Or do you feel like a David in the eyes of others—underrated because of a tainted leader you were under? Take a moment and briefly share your situation. How has your perspective changed after hearing this session?

2. Because David feared the Lord, he left vengeance in God's hands. In fact, when the day came that Saul's life was taken in battle, he didn't rejoice but mourned and taught the Israelite army a love song for Saul (see 2 Samuel 1:11-27). Think back. What was your response the last time someone in authority (a government official, Christian leader, supervisor) had their sin exposed or experienced calamity? What *should* be our response?

   **(Consider checking out Proverbs 24:17-18;
   Obadiah 1:12-15; and Romans 12:20 as a group.)**

3. Abishai was with David on his second chance to take Saul's life—as part of the test. His nagging desire to see Saul dead was the voice of temptation, reminding David that he was justified in killing Saul. But David's choice to put his life—and Saul's—in heaven's hands was what kept him from becoming another Saul. Have you ever had an Abishai in your company, egging you on to get even or making you feel justified in holding grudges? How have you dealt with them? How *should* you deal with them?

4. Like David, have you been treated unfairly or falsely accused by someone in authority? Are you trying to prove your innocence?

While speaking up is the right thing to do at times, ultimately we need to let God handle our case. Carefully read **Isaiah 53:7**; **1 Peter 2:22-23**, and **Genesis 18:25**. What is God saying in these passages about defending yourself?

5. When Samuel saw Jesse's son Eliab, he thought that God *must* have picked him to replace Saul. But God immediately spoke to Samuel and said, "No." He then explained the difference between the way men judge a person's character and the way He judges. Check out **1 Samuel 16:6-7** and **Isaiah 11:1-4** for this explanation. What do these verses say to you about assessing a person's character?

ACTIVITY

When a company executive wants to know how effectively his or her organization is functioning, he or she might conduct an *efficiency audit* to find the areas that need improvement. Guess what? Today is the day for your *leadership audit*. Whether you know it or not, you're leading someone—you are a spiritual father, mother, or mentor to someone.

How effective are you as a leader? Does your leadership style lend itself to be more like Saul or like David? Take a few moments to answer these questions and then share your responses with the group.

- Name two to three people that you are mentoring or have mentored in the past. What role are you playing/did you play in their lives?
- List a few *godly* qualities in your life you'd like them to imitate. What *mistakes* would you want to see them avoid?

- How do you see and/or feel about the people who look to you as a leader? Have you ever wrestled with thoughts of envy, jealousy, or bitterness toward them? If so, do you know why?

SESSION SUMMARY

The most difficult offenses we face are often not with our peers but with people in authority over us. David, who worked under King Saul, is a prime example.

There will be times when God puts us in a place where we have evidence and opportunity to expose the sin of a leader who has wronged us. He usually does this to test our hearts— to see if we'll trust Him and leave judgment in His hands.

To be a man or woman after God's own heart, we must refuse to take revenge on those who've mistreated us. As we trust that He can and will make the right decision, we'll leave vengeance to Him.

While all authority is from God, not all authority is godly. Many times we have to see beyond the leader's *behavior* and honor their God-given *position*.

David's deep sorrow over Saul's death displayed and confirmed the love of God at work in and through his life. As we keep ourselves in the love of God, we can avoid being offended, even with the harshest of leaders.

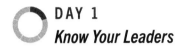

DAY 1
Know Your Leaders

> *. . . Get to know those who labor among you [recognize them for what they are, acknowledge and appreciate and respect them all]—your leaders who are over you in the Lord and those who warn and kindly reprove and exhort you.*
>
> —1 THESSALONIANS 5:12 AMP

From the beginning to the end of our lives, we will always have people in authority over us. God has handpicked leaders to be a part of shaping us into the image of Jesus. Many times our deepest offenses are with these leaders.

Stop and think—who have you worked under that was difficult to serve because of their attitudes, actions, or words? What made it hard for you to submit to their leadership?

_____

_____

_____

_____

_____

_____

David learned many examples of what *not* to do as a result of Saul's harshness. What have you learned *not* to do as a result of being mistreated and overlooked by those in authority?

_____

_____

_____

_____

_____

Name a few people God has placed in your life who serve (or have served) as a spiritual *father* or *mother*. How have they influenced you? What do you appreciate most about them?

_____

_____

_____

_____

Are you struggling with offense toward one of these leaders? If so, who and why? Briefly explain.

_____

_____

_____

_____

What practical steps do you feel God is asking you to take to make things right?

_____

_____

_____

_____

_____

_____

"You must not lose confidence in God because you lost confidence in your pastor. If our confidence in God had to depend upon our confidence in any human person, we would be on shifting sand."—Francis A. Schaeffer[1]

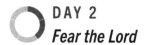

DAY 2
Fear the Lord

> *Fear of the Lord leads to life, bringing*
> *security and protection from harm.*
> —PROVERBS 19:23 NLT

Saul and David both served as kings. Neither were perfect, but there was one characteristic David had that Saul did not—the *fear of the Lord*. It's what kept David from avenging himself by killing Saul when he had the opportunity. It is what positions us to depart from evil: ". . . by the fear of the Lord one departs from evil" (Proverbs 16:6).

What is the fear of the Lord? God gives us some insights in **Deuteronomy 10:12-13** and **Psalm 34:11-14** (see also **1 Peter 3:8-12**). Ponder these passages and write down what He shows you.

_____

_____

_____

_____

David had the chance to kill Saul more than once, but he didn't. Check out **1 Samuel 24:1-15** and **26:7-11**. What do these examples say to you about God? About David? About yourself?

_____

_____

_____

Are *you* living in the fear of the Lord? Or has the fear of people kept you from obeying Him? How can you tell?

_____

_____

_____

_____

God gives us many promises for living in the fear of the Lord. Carefully read these verses and identify the blessings that are yours:

Psalm 111:10 and **Proverbs 1:7**

_____

_____

_____

Proverbs 9:10-11 and **10:27**

_____

_____

_____

Psalm 112:1-3 and **128:1-4**

_____

_____

_____

_____

Psalm 34:9-10; Proverbs 14:26-27; 16:6; and 19:23

_____

_____

_____

_____

"The fear of the Lord is not to be afraid of God; it's to be terrified to be away from Him."—JOHN BEVERE

DAY 3
Cultivate Godly Character

*May you always be filled with the fruit of your salvation—
the righteous character produced in your life by Jesus
Christ—for this will bring much glory and praise to God.*

—PHILIPPIANS 1:11 NLT

David was a man after God's own heart. While he was overlooked by his father and looked down upon by some of his brothers, he had an inner strength and character that God was drawn to.

What was Saul like when God *first* called him to be king? How did he see himself? How is he described in Scripture? Carefully read **1 Samuel 9:2, 17-21**; and **10:20-24** to find the answers.

_____

_____

_____

_____

According to **1 Samuel 13:1-15** and **15:1-26**, what did Saul do that caused God to reject him as king and select David instead? What was he most concerned with?

_____

_____

_____

Henry Blackaby has served as a pastor, church planter, and author for over four decades, passionately helping people experience God. In his book *Chosen to be God's Prophet*, he states:

> "There are no substitutes for obedience . . . . Obedience to God is the key to life! It is the key to the kingdom of God (see Matthew 7:21-24). Obedience is like building your house (life) on a rock. It will not be shaken or moved when the storms of life come (see Luke 6:46-49)."[2]

Is there an area in your life where you know you're *not* obeying God? If so, what is it? What can you learn from Saul's example and personally apply in your life?

_____

_____

_____

_____

_____

_____

God has *good* plans for you! But to live them out, His character has to be developed in you. Carefully read these verses and identify *your part* and *God's part* in the transformation process.

Romans 12:1-2; Philippians 1:6; 2:12-13; Thessalonians 5:23-24; James 1:21-25; and 2 Timothy 3:16-17

MY PART

_____

_____

_____

_____

_____

_____

GOD'S PART

_____

_____

_____

_____

_____

_____

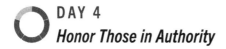

DAY 4
Honor Those in Authority

> *Honor all people. Love the brotherhood.*
> *Fear God. Honor the king.*
> —1 PETER 2:17

According to Scripture, *all* authority is established by God. "For promotion and power come from nowhere on earth, but only from God. He promotes one and deposes another" (Psalm 75:7 TLB). Yet, while all authority is from God, not all authority is godly. Many times we have to see beyond the person's *behavior* and honor their God-given position.

Carefully read **Romans 13:1-7**. What insights about leadership is God showing you in this passage? How does it challenge you?

_____

_____

_____

_____

_____

_____

_____

_____

Are there any people in authority in your life that you were *convinced* were not established by God? If so, who? Why did you feel this way? How did you treat them in response?

_____

_____

_____

_____

_____

_____

Under what circumstance are we *not* to obey human authority? Even in this situation, what should be our attitude?

_____

_____

_____

_____

_____

_____

Check out Shadrach, Meshach, and Abednego's response
to King Nebuchadnezzar in Daniel 3:8-18.

God tells us to *honor* our leaders—regardless of their behavior. Take time to read these passages. Name a few practical ways to honor authority. Why does God ask us to do this?

Exodus 22:28 and **Ecclesiastes 10:20**

_____

_____

_____

_____

1 Timothy 2:1-4

_____

_____

_____

Titus 3:1-2 and **1 Peter 2:13-20**

_____

_____

_____

_____

DAY 5
Keep Yourself in God's Love

Guard and keep yourselves in the love of God . . . .
—JUDE 1:21 AMP

Another way to avoid being offended with those in authority is to live in the love of God. His love gives us strength! It casts out all fear, empowers us to forgive, and enables us to release and bless those who've mistreated us.

According to **Romans 5:8** and **1 John 4:9-10**, how does God *demonstrate* His love for us?

_____

_____

_____

_____

Also consider Ephesians 2:4-5.

"The springs of love are in God, not in us. It is absurd to look
for the love of God in our hearts naturally; it is only there when
it has been shed abroad in our hearts by the Holy Spirit."
—OSWALD CHAMBERS[3]

God's love also enables us to see people the way He sees them and not to judge based on outward appearances or behavior. Take time to meditate on God's detailed description of love in **1 Corinthians**

13:4-8. What is He showing you in this passage about His love *for you* and His love *in you* for others?

_____

_____

_____

_____

Consider reading this passage in the Amplified Bible.

Romans 5:5 tells us that ". . . God's love has been poured out in our hearts through the Holy Spirit Who has been given to us" (AMP). He wants His love to grow in us more and more. In your own words, describe what **1 John 4:12, 16-17** says about how God's love matures in us.

_____

_____

_____

_____

Consider David's reaction when he heard of Saul's death. How does his response challenge you to walk in God's love and change your response toward the leadership that has mistreated you?

_____

_____

_____

Out of His glorious, unlimited resources He will give you the mighty inner strengthening of His Holy Spirit. And I pray that Christ will be more and more at home in your hearts, living within you as you trust in Him. May your roots go down deep into the soil of God's marvelous love; and may you be able to feel and understand, as all God's children should, how long, how wide, how deep, and how high His love really is; and to experience this love for yourselves . . . . —EPHESIANS 3:16-19 TLB

FOOD FOR THOUGHT . . .

All of us will have opportunities to be offended with and expose leaders who've hurt us and made mistakes. God allows this test—to see if we'll take matters into our own hands or trust Him to bring vengeance. Seize this opportunity to identify the leaders in your life who've treated you like Saul treated David—attacking and falsely accusing you at every turn. How have you thought and spoken of them? What changes do you feel God is asking you to make in your thoughts, words, and attitudes? Pour your heart out on paper, capturing the insight He gives you.

JOURNAL

_____

_____

_____

_____

_____

_____

_____

_____

_____

_____

_____

_____

_____

_____

_____

_____

_____

(1) Quotes by *Francis A. Schaeffer* (http://www.azquotes.com/author/13063-Francis_Schaeffer /tag/god, accessed 10/27/16). (2) Henry Blackaby, *Chosen to be God's Prophet* (Nashville, TN: Thomas Nelson Publishers, 2003) pp. 167, 178. (3) Oswald Chambers, *My Utmost for His Highest* (Uhrichsville, OH: Barbour Publishing, 1997) p. 121.

"There are going to be times when people say things about you to slander and defame your character. The question is, are you going to live by Jesus's example and obey your calling? Or are you going to defend yourself? You can defend yourself and win, but you'll miss out on the blessing. The choice is up to you."

—JOHN BEVERE

CHAPTER 4

How to Handle Unfair Treatment

OVERVIEW

- **Get Started:** Welcome the group and ask them this question: "Have you ever had a leader with a personal vendetta toward you? Someone who was constantly doing and saying rude things to you? How did you react to their face? How did you react behind their back?" Allow a few people to share their experiences. Let everyone know that Session 4 includes two great examples of how to handle direct, personal attacks *without* becoming bitter. Encourage them to listen for the attitudes of those under attack, and the way God chose to vindicate them.

- **Pray:** When we're offended, our gut reaction is to begin defending ourselves, especially when we've been falsely accused. But if we do that, we'll miss out on God's blessings. Pray and ask the Lord to deposit into each person the *power* and *desire* not to take matters into their own hands—to bless their offender and trust God to make things right in His time.

- **Watch:** View **Session 4** of *The Bait of Satan Study* together.

- **Discuss**: Endurance is one of the most important qualities of any successful athlete, business owner, or parent. Ask everyone, "What is *endurance* and how do we build it? How might having endurance benefit us in overcoming offense?" Allow a few people to share their thoughts and then guide the group into the discussion questions for Chapter 4.

- **Read:** This week we recommend that you read chapters 7-10 in *The Bait of Satan* book. The content shared in these chapters will be supplemental to the content shared in Session 4.

- **Devotions**: This week's devotions focus on staying confident in God's ability, letting Him be your Defender, blessing your enemies, and planting seeds of love and mercy. Once more, direct the group to invest a few minutes each day to carefully read through each devotion and answer the questions honestly.

- **Journal**: One valuable aspect of learning during this study is to write down any insights God reveals along the way. As the group travels through the video, discussion questions, and devotions, remind them to take notes. The wisdom they receive is a treasure.

GROUP DISCUSSION QUESTIONS

1. In your own words, how would you define *unfair treatment*? What kind is the most difficult for you to deal with? Why?

2. God has promised to repay those who have harshly treated us. Sometimes His repayment doesn't come in the form of punishment—it comes in the form of the salvation of the person who has wronged us. If this were to happen to an enemy of yours, what would be your reaction? Why? What does this say about the condition of your heart?

3. While some verses in Scripture are uplifting, others are considerably harder to swallow. When you run across passages like these, what do you normally do? Do you choose to *believe what you read* or *read into Scripture* what you believe? Do you ignore these verses altogether or gloss over them quickly? What should be our response to the more difficult passages of truth?

    (Consider checking out 2 Peter 1:20-21; James 1:21; and 2 Timothy 3:16-17 as a group.)

4. When we are being treated cruelly and unjustly again and again, we not only need God's strength to endure, but also His wisdom to know what to do. As a group, read **James 3:13-18** and identify the differences between *ungodly wisdom* and *godly wisdom*. What results can you expect from listening to and using each?

5. In light of the answers from question 4, what is the difference between Satan spotlighting someone's faults and God revealing them? What feelings or thoughts might be connected or experienced with each? What actions do they drive us to take?

ACTIVITY

For this week's activity, get a pen and paper and *write a brief letter to God* describing in detail how someone close to you hurt you deeply. Then, by faith, release them into God's hands. He will deal with them, but pray for Him to show them mercy and give them grace to cooperate with His dealings. (A sample prayer is provided.)

Once everyone has written their letter, prayed, and released their offender into God's hands, take all the letters and run them through a paper shredder. (If a paper shredder is unavailable, have everyone tear their letter into tiny pieces.) Collect the pieces and say, "Just as the details in these letters are no longer recognizable, may the memory and effects of your mistreatment no longer be recognizable or felt by me."

My Letter to God

_____

_____

_____

_____

_____

_____

_____

_____

PRAYER OF COMMITMENT

Father, I have shared my heart with You and written down what _____ *(person's name) did to hurt me. Please forgive me for holding on to any unforgiveness toward them. I want to forgive them, but I need Your strength to do it. So, as an act of my will—not my feelings—I release them into Your hands. I trust You to deal with them in Your time, in Your way, and I will not avenge myself. Please have mercy on them and give them a heart that will hear and respond to Your voice. Please heal the hurts in my soul—the painful memories and feelings that have remained. Give me the grace to trust You with my life and to submit to the leaders that You place over me. Your Word says that You'll work all things together for my good because I love You and I am pursuing Your purpose for my life* (see Romans 8:28). *I'm trusting You to faithfully fulfill Your promise. In Jesus's name, Amen!*

SESSION SUMMARY

○ God's instruction to not avenge ourselves is a command, not a suggestion. We can trust Him to make things right in His time and His way. This confidence is a righteous thing in His eyes.

○ When we're falsely accused, God Himself will defend us if we let Him. He's the greatest Attorney the universe has ever known—and He's never lost a case.

○ We are called to submit to *all* our leaders, whether they're good and gentle or harsh and unreasonable. To fulfill this calling, we need Christ's supernatural strength living in and through us.

○ God's way for us to deal with a leader's unjust treatment is to humble ourselves and bless them. By praying a blessing on them, we will receive a blessing.

○ What we plant, we will harvest. As we continue to plant seeds of love, mercy, peace, and forgiveness, we'll eventually reap a harvest of the same. Good seed produces a good harvest.

DAY 1
Be Confident in God's Ability

In God have I put my trust and confident reliance;
I will not be afraid. What can man do to me?
—PSALM 56:11 AMP

When we're mistreated, we're tempted many times to get even. Again and again God reminds us in His Word that He will repay, as long as we don't take matters into our own hands.

Carefully read **Romans 12:17-19; Proverbs 20:22; 24:19-20, 29;** and **Deuteronomy 32:35-36.** What promise(s) does God make to us, His people? What conditions does He ask us to meet?

_____

_____

_____

Hannah Whitall Smith was an author and lay speaker from the mid-1800s to the early 1900s. Having lived through the turbulence of the Civil War and having mourned the loss of four of her seven children, she was no stranger to hard times. She stated:

"We are not to avenge ourselves, because our Father has charged Himself with our defense. We are not to fear, for the Lord is on our side. No one can be against us, because He is for us. . . .

No man or company of men, no power in earth or heaven, can touch that soul which is abiding in Christ, without first passing through Him, and receiving the seal of His permission. If God is for us, it matters not who may be against us."[1]

Take a few minutes to meditate on the *supreme strength* of God in these Scriptures. As you read through them, identify the facets of His power and share how they encourage you to trust Him.

2 Samuel 22:3; Psalm 28:6-8; and Proverbs 30:5

_____

_____

_____

Daniel 6:26-27; 2 Chronicles 20:6; Isaiah 43:13; and Psalm 135:5-13

_____

_____

_____

Isaiah 40:10-12; 25-31; Psalm 95:3-5; and Jeremiah 32:17

_____

_____

_____

_____

Also consider God's response to Job in Job 38.

These passages encourage me to trust God by . . .

_____

_____

_____

_____

_____

_____

The Lord God is my Strength, my personal bravery, and my invincible army; He makes my feet like hinds' feet and will make me to walk [not to stand still in terror, but to walk] and make [spiritual] progress upon my high places [of trouble, suffering, or responsibility]!—HABAKKUK 3:19 AMP

DAY 2
Let God Be Your Defender

*With dread deeds and awesome power You
will defend us from our enemies, O God who
saves us. You are the only hope of all mankind
throughout the world and far away upon the sea.*

—PSALM 65:5 TLB

God is our Defender! He loves us more than we can ever compre-
hend and wants us to trust Him to meet every need, especially His
unmatched ability to be our Advocate.

A.W. Tozer strengthened countless hungry souls and pierced
hearts with his dynamic insights in the early twentieth century. In his
classic book *Born after Midnight*, he urges:

> "It is vitally important that we move up into the Spirit and
> cease to defend ourselves. I have never met a victorious Chris-
> tian who was on the defensive, but I have met, I cannot tell
> how many jumpy, skittish and thoroughly unhappy Christians
> who were burning up their energies in a vain endeavor to pro-
> tect themselves. . . . My earnest advice to all such nervous souls
> is to turn everything over to God and relax. A real Christian
> need not defend his possession nor his position. God will take
> care of both."[2]

Has your job ever been in jeopardy because you stood for truth and did the right thing? Have you been harshly treated for refusing to compromise or sin? If so, explain the situation.

_____

_____

_____

_____

Has God ever asked you to go and apologize to a harsh leader? If yes, who was it? Have you done it? If you have, what was the leader's response? How did you feel afterward?

_____

_____

_____

If you haven't apologized, what's holding you back? What is God saying to you in this chapter?

_____

_____

_____

_____

_____

Be careful not to jump to conclusions before the Lord returns as to whether someone is a good servant or not. When the Lord comes, He will turn on the light so that everyone can see exactly what each one of us is really like, deep down in our hearts. Then everyone will know why we have been doing the Lord's work. At that time God will give to each one whatever praise is coming to him.—1 Corinthians 4:5 TLB

When we're falsely accused and treated unfairly, our natural response is often to begin judging. Carefully read Jesus's words of warning in **Matthew 7:1-5** and **Luke 6:37-42**. What can we expect to happen if we judge? What do we need to be careful of? What else is God showing you?

_____

_____

_____

_____

_____

Also consider God's caution signs in Romans 14:10-13 and James 4:11-12.

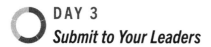

DAY 3
Submit to Your Leaders

> *Servants [employees, students, team members, etc.],*
> *be submissive to your masters [employers, teachers,*
> *managers, supervisors, etc.] with all fear, not only*
> *to the good and gentle, but also to the harsh.*
> —1 PETER 2:18

[Words in brackets added for clarity and emphasis.]

God wants us to submit to those in authority over us. Even Jesus Himself, who was fully God, submitted to the will of the Father by giving His life so that we could have new life in Him.

In your own words and in practical terms, describe what *submitting* to people in authority may look like. What might *resisting* authority look like?

_____

_____

_____

_____

_____

Consider Ephesians 4:1-7, 23-32 and 1 Thessalonians 5:12-15.

Imagine *you* are the one in charge at work, church, etc. How would you want people to submit to and honor you as their leader? Are you doing these things? If not, why?

_____

_____

_____

_____

By definition, a *harsh* leader is one who is "crooked, cruel, perverse, dishonest, unjust, and tyrannical." Submitting to a leader like this will take more than willpower. It takes Christ's power—the supernatural strength of His Spirit. Take time to *meditate* on these passages:

He gives power to the faint and weary, and to him who has no might He increases strength [causing it to multiply and making it to abound].—ISAIAH 40:29 AMP

I have strength for all things in Christ Who empowers me [I am ready for anything and equal to anything through Him Who infuses inner strength into me; I am self-sufficient in Christ's sufficiency].—PHILIPPIANS 4:13 AMP

He gives us more and more grace (power of the Holy Spirit, to meet this evil tendency and all others fully). That is why He says, God sets Himself against the proud and haughty, but gives grace [continually] to the lowly (those who are humble enough to receive it).—JAMES 4:6 AMP

I thank Christ Jesus our Lord, who has given me strength to do His work. He considered me trustworthy and appointed me to serve Him.—1 TIMOTHY 1:12 NLT

What is God showing you in these verses about the strength He's made available to you?

_____

_____

_____

_____

_____

Also consider Psalm 28:8; 46:1-2; and 73:25-26.

How do you receive His strength? Read **John 14:13-14; 15:7;** and **1 John 5:14-15** for the answer.

_____

_____

_____

_____

_____

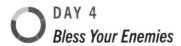

DAY 4
Bless Your Enemies

> *"But I say to all of you who will listen to me: love your*
> *enemies, do good to those who hate you, bless those who*
> *curse you, and pray for those who treat you badly."*
> —LUKE 6:27-28 PHILLIPS

There are several steps in the forgiveness process. The first is *recogniz-ing and admitting* to God and yourself that you've been hurt. *Asking Him to forgive you* for holding on to offense and unforgiveness toward the person is the next step, which is followed by *releasing the offender* into God's hands. The crucial step that we often forget or omit is to *pray for and bless our enemy.*

Our natural reaction when we're badly treated is to pay back in-sult for insult, hurt for hurt. The *super*natural response—the one we're *called* to—is different. Read **1 Peter 3:8-9** and explain it.

_____

_____

_____

What has God promised us in return for obeying this calling? What are we to guard against? [Hint: Our choice to do this confirms we fear God (see **1 Peter 3:10-12** and **Psalm 34:11-15**)].

_____

_____

_____

God is clear in **Proverbs 25:21-22** and **Romans 12:14, 17-21** about how He wants us to treat to our enemies. What is He saying in these verses, and what new insights is He showing you?

_____

_____

_____

In what practical ways is God encouraging you to fulfill this calling with your leaders?

_____

_____

_____

> Blessed are you when people hate you, avoid you, insult you, and slander you because you are committed to the Son of Man (GW). When that happens, rejoice! Yes, leap for joy! For you will have a great reward awaiting you in heaven. And you will be in good company—the ancient prophets were treated that way too!—LUKE 6:22-23 TLB

It's crucial to keep in mind who the _real_ enemy is. **Ephesians 6:12** and **1 Peter 5:8-9** identify them. How do these truths help you see your situation in a different light and temper your response?

_____

_____

_____

DAY 5
Plant Good Seed

> *"Plant the good seeds of righteousness, and you will*
> *reap a crop of My love; plow the hard ground of your*
> *hearts, for now is the time to seek the Lord, that He*
> *may come and shower salvation upon you."*
> —HOSEA 10:12 TLB

Seeds are amazing! They produce, after their kind, an entirely mature plant from a tiny kernel. Just like physical seeds, there are invisible, intangible seeds we're planting all the time. Our attitudes, actions, and words are all seeds we sow into the souls of others that will produce fruit—either good or bad.

One of the most important principles to understand about seeds is in **Galatians 6:7-8**. Meditate on this passage and in your own words, describe the Law of Sowing and Reaping as it relates to spiritual issues and life in general.

_____

_____

_____

_____

_____

_____

The Golden Rule was given to us by Jesus in **Matthew 7:12** and **Luke 6:31**. Take a moment to write out this treasured truth. What connection can you see between it and the Law of Sowing and Reaping?

_____

_____

_____

And those who are peacemakers will plant seeds of peace and reap a harvest of righteousness.—JAMES 3:18 NLT

Stop and think: _What kinds of seeds am I sowing? What attitudes, actions, and words am I planting in others—especially my family, closest friends, and most frustrating enemies?_

_____

_____

_____

_____

In light of your previous answer, what kind of harvest can you expect? Do you need to pray for a "crop failure"? What changes do you feel God is asking you to make in your planting?

_____

_____

_____

Offense is also a seed. If nurtured, it puts down *roots* of bitterness in our hearts and begins to grow. Carefully read **Hebrews 12:14-15** and **James 3:14-16**. Why is bitterness so dangerous? What can happen if it's left unchecked? What steps can you take to stop it from growing in you?

_____

_____

_____

_____

**Also check out Ephesians 4:17-32 and reflect back
on your answers in this chapter's activity.**

FOOD FOR THOUGHT . . .

God has made it extremely clear that revenge is His job—not ours—and that the only right path to take when we've been attacked is to wait for Him to settle the score. Unfair treatment is an opportunity to pay back with a blessing, knowing that it's our calling which enables us to inherit a blessing.

At this midpoint in the study, what's God shining His searchlight on in you? What areas of your character is He renovating? How's He setting you up to get blessed if you handle things right? Take time now and ask God to open your eyes to the truth about Him, your situations, and yourself. Pour your heart out on paper, capturing the insight He gives you.

_____

_____

_____

_____

_____

_____

_____

_____

_____

_____

_____

_____

_____

_____

(1) Hannah Whitall Smith, *The Christian's Secret to a Happy Life* (Gainesville, FL: Bridge-Logos, 1998) pp. 120, 122. (2) A.W. Tozer, *Born after Midnight* (Camp Hill, PA: Christian Publications, 1989) pp. 98-99.

"The debt we were forgiven was unpayable. There was no way we could ever repay God what we owed Him. . . . A person who cannot forgive has forgotten the great debt for which they were forgiven. When you realize that Jesus delivered you from eternal death and torment, you will release others unconditionally."

—JOHN BEVERE

CHAPTER 5

Escaping the Trap

OVERVIEW

- **Get Started:** After welcoming the group to Session 5, ask the question: "Have you ever *graded* some sins as worse than others? What things have you considered 'weaknesses' in your own life while calling full-blown *sin* in the lives of others?" Allow a few people to share their examples, and then let everyone know that this session will focus on God's perspective of sin and His divine ability to forgive.

- **Pray:** When we or someone close to us has been severely hurt, holding on to unforgiveness can seem logical—even justified—in our own minds. It's human nature to think that there's no reason or ability to forgive an offender. Ask God to open each participant's eyes to recognize their *need* to forgive and to know He has given them the power and desire to do it.

- **Watch:** View **Session 5** of *The Bait of Satan Study* together.

- **Discuss**: In this session, John states that if we treat the "little" sins as if they were "big" sins, the chances of getting free go way up. Ask the group, "Imagine: What would your life look like if you were free of the sins that easily trip you up? What practical steps can we take and encourage others to take to throw off these nagging sins?" Listen and use the group's answers as a catalyst to begin the Chapter 5 discussion questions.

- **Read:** This week we recommend that you read chapters 11-12 in *The Bait of Satan* book.

- **Devotions**: This week's devotions deal with the price of forgiveness, the need to forgive, what it means to take the high road, and growing in God's grace. Once again, ask the group to invest a few minutes daily to carefully read through each devotion and answer the questions honestly.

- **Journal**: Writing down the revelation of truth God speaks to us is something He's been telling His people to do for thousands of years. As you watch the teaching, participate in the group discussion, work through the devotions, and remind everyone to record the insights the Holy Spirit speaks to their hearts. His words are life-changing!

GROUP DISCUSSION QUESTIONS

1. Again and again throughout the New Testament, we are taught—even urged—to forgive others. In your own words,

describe what it means to forgive. If you had hurt someone and needed forgiveness, how would you want them to treat you? What would you want them to say and do?

2. Just as everyone needs to shower or bathe regularly to be cleaned of physical dirt, we all need forgiveness regularly to be free of spiritual dirt (sin). What do you think your life would be like if you were forbidden to take a shower, wash your hair, or brush your teeth for a month—or a year? How would your life be if God withheld His forgiveness from you for a month? What if He withheld it forever? Take a few moments to explain.

3. Jesus shares powerful principles on forgiveness in the parable of the unmerciful servant in **Matthew 18:21-35**. Carefully read this passage as a group and answer these questions:
   a. Who is Jesus speaking to and how can you tell?
   b. When Jesus told Peter to forgive *seventy times seven*, what was He really saying?
   c. What two things happened to the servant who demanded that his fellow servant repay him?
   d. Who do the torturers represent?
   e. What is God showing you in this parable that you can apply in your life?

4. Think back to our opening questions. Have you looked at unforgiveness as a weakness instead of a sin? How has your view of this changed after hearing John's message? What are some of the dangers of categorizing sin?

5. John's account of the youth pastor was a story of triple betrayal: His pastor and mentor had an affair with his wife; she left him and then he was fired by the church board. Years later, he became a senior pastor and saw both his exwife and his former pastor come to his church. He then had a choice: welcome them or push them out. He took the high road by forgiving them and even allowing them to serve in his church. How do you think he was able to forgive on such a huge scale? Could you do the same?

6. Remember the story about J.R.? He'd been trapped in a lifestyle of sin and had reached out to John for prayer. Expecting to be judged and rejected, J.R. was shocked when John chose to look past his lifestyle to see his heart, which was searching for God. Have you ever been in a situation like this? If you have, how did you respond? Would you react any differently now? If so, how?

ACTIVITY

Corrie Ten Boom said, "The best learning I had came from *teaching*."[1] Imagine you are the teacher and that the people in your group are those you *deeply* love and don't want to see fall into the trap of offense.

Take a few moments to stop and think. What would you share with your closest and dearest friends to help them *avoid* the trap of offense? What's helping you stay free from offense? List two or more specific things the Lord has taught and revealed to you through these lessons. Include any scriptures that He has made alive to you along the way.

As a teacher, I would tell my friends to *avoid* the trap of offense by...

_____

_____

_____

_____

Now let's change things up a bit. You're still the teacher and the people in your group are still those closest to you, but this time they're *already offended*. Their lives are becoming more miserable by the day. They don't want to live the way they're living, but they don't know what's wrong or how to change it.

Again, stop and think. What would you share with your closest friends to help them recognize and *escape* the trap of offense? What's helped you break free from the prison of offense? List two or more specific things God has taught and revealed to you through these lessons and any specific scriptures He's used to strengthen you on your journey.

As a teacher, I would tell my friends to *escape* the trap of offense by...

_____

_____

_____

_____

O A person who cannot forgive is one who has forgotten what they've been forgiven of. We've each been forgiven an unpayable debt and rescued from eternal punishment by the mercy of God.

O In order to experience the grandness of God's forgiveness, we have to extend forgiveness to others. He reminds us of this again and again in His Word.

O No matter how we categorize it, sin is sin. This applies to unforgiveness too—it is sin, not just a *weakness*. Guarding ourselves from this trap is vital.

O Whenever we encounter offense, we'll come out of it changed; what we do with it will determine our future. Our options are either bitter or better—there's no in between.

O You *do* have the ability to forgive any offense because the love of God has been poured into your heart. As you continue to receive His forgiveness, know that you can extend that same forgiveness and grace to others.

DAY 1
Remember the Price of Forgiveness

For God sent Christ Jesus to take the punishment for our sins and to end all God's anger against us. He used Christ's blood and our faith as the means of saving us from His wrath . . . .
—ROMANS 3:25 TLB

To *forgive* means "to send forth, send away; to completely cancel debts or sins." To receive forgiveness "indicates the remission—the release or dismissal—of sin and the punishment due to the sinful conduct; the deliverance of the sinner from the divine penalty."[2]

How do we receive forgiveness for things we've done wrong? Can we be sure we're forgiven?

_____

_____

_____

_____

_____

_____

Check out 1 John 1:8-9; 2:1-2; 1 Peter 2:24; Titus 3:3-7; Psalm 103:8-12; and Isaiah 43:25.

Look back over your life. Can you remember any *habits* or *ways of thinking* you're no longer chained to—things God has forgiven and set you free from? What are they?

_____

_____

_____

_____

"Forgiveness is the key that unlocks the door of resentment and the handcuffs of hatred. It is a power that breaks the chains of bitterness and the shackles of selfishness."—CORRIE TEN BOOM[3]

What was the *cost* of our forgiveness? Carefully read **Ephesians 1:6-8; 1 Peter 1:18-22;** and **Revelation 1:5** for the answer.

_____

_____

_____

_____

How does remembering your past mistakes and the price paid for your forgiveness help you let go of offenses more willingly?

_____

_____

_____

Jesus gave His life to save us from what we deserved—separation from God forever. While the subject isn't popular, it's one God talks about extensively. What is hell like? Check out these verses:

Matthew 8:12; 13:42, 50; 22:13; 25:30; 25:41, 46; Mark 9:44; Luke 16:23-24; 2 Thessalonians 1:9; Jude 6, and **13 Revelation 14:10-11; 20:10**

_____

_____

_____

_____

How do these passages give you a greater sense of gratitude for what Jesus did? How do they motivate you to pray and help others?

_____

_____

_____

_____

DAY 2
Forgive and You'll Be Forgiven

. . . Freely you have received, freely give.
—MATTHEW 10:8

God says that we've all been contaminated by sin and fallen short of
His perfect standard (see Isaiah 64:6 and Romans 3:23). Thankfully,
He's ready and willing to forgive us of every sin, every time we come
to Him. There's only one condition to His forgiveness.

Take time to meditate on these verses about *receiving* and *giving*
forgiveness.

For if you forgive people their trespasses [their reckless and
willful sins, leaving them, letting them go, and giving up resent-
ment], your heavenly Father will also forgive you. But if you
do not forgive others their trespasses [their reckless and willful
sins, leaving them, letting them go, and giving up resentment],
neither will your Father forgive you your trespasses.—MATTHEW
6:14-15 AMP

"And when you assume the posture of prayer, remember that it's
not all asking. If you have anything against someone, forgive—
only then will your heavenly Father be inclined to also wipe
your slate clean of sins."—MARK 11:24-25 MSG

". . . For He is kind to the unthankful and evil. Therefore be merciful, just as your Father also is merciful. Judge not, and you shall

not be judged. Condemn not, and you shall not be condemned. Forgive, and you will be forgiven."—LUKE 6:35-37

Make a clean break with all cutting, backbiting, profane talk. Be gentle with one another, sensitive. Forgive one another as quickly and thoroughly as God in Christ forgave you.—EPHE-SIANS 4:32 MSG

What is God speaking to you about forgiveness and the consequences of holding on to offense?

_____

_____

_____

_____

_____

If God doesn't forgive us, our sins remain on us—a dangerous condition to be in. What are the side effects of this condition? Read **Isaiah 59:1-3** and **Psalm 32:3-7** and explain what happens.

_____

_____

_____

_____

_____

"'Forgive us our sins as we forgive those that sin against us.' There is no slightest suggestion that we are offered forgiveness on any other terms. It is made perfectly clear that if we do not forgive we shall not be forgiven. There are no two ways about it."—C.S. Lewis[4]

Have you forgiven *yourself?* God wants you to—no matter what your past might be. Write down anything you've done that's been hard to let go of and give it to Him. Ask for and receive His forgiveness; trust Him, and go on.

DAY 3
Guard Your Mouth

Words kill, words give life; they're either
poison or fruit—you choose.
—PROVERBS 18:21 MSG

There are seven things that God says He *hates* in Proverbs 6:16-19. Interestingly, three of them involve one of our most underrated forces: our words. While many Christians today consider adultery and murder as major issues, they see things like gossip and slander as minor—even justifiable. To break free and stay free of offense, we must learn to carefully steward our words.

Sin is *sin*—no matter how we classify it. What kinds of sin have been easier for you to dismiss as simply a *weakness*? Which ones have you classified as *bigger* or *worse*? Why is this?

_____

_____

_____

_____

_____

When someone's flaws are painfully obvious, it's often difficult to keep quiet. Thank God His love covers all our sin (see 1 Peter 4:8)! Carefully read these verses and explain the value in refusing to verbally spotlight other people's faults. What else is God speaking to you?

Proverbs 10:18-21; 17:27-28; and 26:20

_____

_____

_____

_____

Ephesians 4:29-30; Titus 3:1-2; James 4:11-12; and 1 Peter 2:1-3

_____

_____

_____

_____

Psalm 34:12-14 and Proverbs 13:3; 17:9; 21:23

_____

_____

_____

_____

Meditate on Psalm 141:1-4 and make it a prayer
from your heart to God.

Whoever goes about slandering reveals secrets, but he who
is trustworthy in spirit keeps a thing covered.—PROVERBS
11:13 ESV

Guarding our mouth against destructive speech is a key part of forgiveness. What would it look like to begin covering offenses instead of highlighting them? How might your life and relationships improve?

_____

_____

_____

_____

Take another look at today's verse. How does knowing the power of your words encourage you to think twice before letting whatever comes to mind pop out of your mouth?

_____

_____

_____

_____

"Words are seeds. What we speak, we sow, and what we sow, we reap! . . . Keep yourself happy by being careful about what comes out of your mouth."—JOYCE MEYER[5]

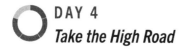

DAY 4
Take the High Road

Good sense makes a man restrain his anger, and it is
his glory to overlook a transgression or an offense.

—PROVERBS 19:11 AMP

When someone offends us, we will take one of two roads: the low road, which leads to pain and bitterness, or the high road, which leads to a better, healthier life. For over twenty-five years, family physician and nutritionist Don Colbert, M.D. has personally observed this. He states:

"I consider *bitterness, resentment* and *unforgiveness* to be among the *deadliest* emotions a person can have. They can actually prevent the body from releasing toxic material—generally creating an acidic condition in the tissues. This buildup of toxins in the system can eventually lead to *disease*."[6]

Have you ever been angry with someone for a long time? If so, how did it eventually affect you (*physically, mentally,* and *emotionally*)? What effects did it have on your relationship with God?

_____

_____

_____

_____

Michal, David's wife, was offended and bitter with him over the way he worshipped God when the Ark of the Lord came back to Israel. Read the story in **2 Samuel 6:12-23**. What happened to Michal as a result of bitterness? What does this say to you personally?

_____

_____

_____

_____

_____

_____

Consider also Cain and what happened to him when he became offended and bitter with Abel and God (see Genesis 4:1-16).

The _high road_ is the one of forgiveness. Its effects are life-giving. Dr. Colbert confirms this:

"Forgiveness releases layers of hurt and heals the raw, jagged edges of emotional pain. It enables a person to release buried anger, resentment, bitterness, shame, grief, regret, guilt, hate, and other _toxic_ emotions that hide deep in the soul, making a person ill—both emotionally and physically."[7]

The high road is paved with kindness, compassion, and mercy—it's the path God takes when dealing with us (see Lamentations 3:22-23). Carefully read **Micah 6:8; Matthew 5:7; James 2:13; Luke 6:35-38;**

and **Proverbs 3:1-4.** What wisdom is God showing you that you can apply in your life?

_____

_____

_____

_____

_____

His compassion never ends. It is only the Lord's mercies that have kept us from complete destruction. Great is His faithfulness; His loving-kindness begins afresh each day.—LAMENTATIONS 3:22-23 TLB

DAY 5
Get Rooted and Grow in Grace

> *Grow in grace (undeserved favor, spiritual strength)*
> *and recognition and knowledge and understanding of*
> *our Lord and Savior Jesus Christ (the Messiah) . . . .*
> —2 PETER 3:18 AMP

Grace. It is God's undeserved favor and power to do what we could never do on our own. It's His ability to forgive the unforgivable offenses of others and escape the trap of offense. All of us have received God's grace through faith in Jesus, and we *grow* in grace by abiding in Him.

Take a few moments to meditate on these verses.

And now just as you trusted Christ to save you, trust Him, too, for each day's problems; live in vital union with Him. Let your roots grow down into Him and draw up nourishment from Him. See that you go on growing in the Lord, and become strong and vigorous in the truth you were taught. Let your lives overflow with joy and thanksgiving for all He has done.—COLOSSIANS 2:6-7 TLB

Out of His glorious, unlimited resources He will give you the mighty inner strengthening of His Holy Spirit. And I pray that Christ will be more and more at home in your hearts, living within you as you trust in Him. May your roots go down deep into the soil of God's marvelous love; and may you be able to feel and understand, as all God's children should, how long, how wide, how deep, and how high His love really is; and to experience this love for yourselves, though it is so great that you will never see the end of it or fully know or understand it. And so at last you will be filled up with God Himself.—EPHE-SIANS 3:16-19 TLB

What is God revealing to you about *Himself* and about *you* in these passages? What practical steps can you take to experience more quality time with Him and deepen your roots?

_____

_____

_____

_____

_____

Galatians 5:22-23 reveals nine fruits of God's character that grow in us as we live in Him. Which of these fruits are most evident in your life? Which ones need more development?

_____

_____

_____

_____

_____

According to **Hebrews 12:14-15; Galatians 2:19-21;** and **2 Corinthians 6:1-2,** we can *miss* or *fall short* of God's grace. In your own words, what does this mean? How does it happen and how can it be avoided?

_____

_____

_____

_____

_____

But He gives us more and more grace (power of the Holy Spirit, to meet this evil tendency and all others fully). That is why He says, God sets Himself against the proud and haughty, but gives grace [continually] to the lowly (those who are humble enough to receive it).—JAMES 4:6 AMP

FOOD FOR THOUGHT . . .

Refusing to forgive means we've forgotten the unpayable debt Jesus forgave us. This blocks His forgiveness from flowing into our lives and locks us in a state of misery. The good news is there's a way out! In Christ, you have the *power* and *desire* to forgive.

Reflect for a moment on the biggest battles you've fought with unforgiveness. Are you ready to win? Get quiet with God. Ask Him to give you the strength you need to release any grudges you've been holding. Pour your heart out on paper, capturing the insight He gives you.

JOURNAL

_____

_____

_____

_____

_____

_____

_____

_____

_____

_____

_____

_____

(1) Quotes on _Learning_ by Corrie Ten Boom (http://www.christianquotes.info/quotes-by-author/corrie-ten-boom-quotes/, accessed 11/16/16). (2) Adapted from _Vine's Complete Expository Dictionary of Old and New Testament Words_, W.E. Vine (Nashville, TN: Thomas Nelson Publishing, 1996). (3) Corrie Ten Boom. AZQuotes.com, (Wind and Fly LTD, 2016. www.azquotes.com/quote/450732, accessed 11/15/16). (4) C.S. Lewis, _The Joyful Christian_ (New York, NY: Macmillan Publishing Company, 1977) p. 142. (5) Joyce Meyer, _Enjoying Where You Are on the Way to Where You Are Going_ (Tulsa, OK: Harrison House, Inc., 1996) pp. 203, 206. (6) _The Cleansing Power of Forgiveness_, Don Colbert, M.D. (Enjoying Everyday Life magazine, May 2006, Joyce Meyer Ministries, Inc., Fenton, MO) pp. 29-30. (7) Ibid.

"Since we are to imitate God, we are to extend reconciliation to a brother who sins against us. Jesus established this pattern: Go to him and show him his sin, not to condemn him but to remove anything that lies between the two of you and thus be reconciled and restored. The goodness of God within us will draw our brother to repentance and restoration of the relationship."

—JOHN BEVERE

CHAPTER 6

Reconciliation

OVERVIEW

- **Get Started:** Commend everyone for making it to the final session! Seeking a closer walk with God is always something to celebrate. As things settle down, ask the group: "Have you wondered what would happen if you tried to get free from offense, but just couldn't seem to shake it? Is there a certain person you've found especially difficult to forgive?" Listen as people share their stories. Then tell everyone that Session 6 explains the path to freedom from offense in great detail. Encourage them to listen and look through the lens of their own lives, receiving the wisdom that they need personally.

- **Pray:** You and your group are about to take the final steps to the life-defining moment we talked about in Chapter 1. Pray and ask God to cultivate in each person a sincere willingness to forgive and bless their enemies and to speak just what they need to hear to get free and stay free of offense. May this chapter be the game changer in the lives of everyone participating, in Jesus's name!

- **Watch**: View **Session 6** of *The Bait of Satan Study* together.

- **Discuss**: Ask the group: "Like John, have you ever experienced a time when the love of God in you had grown cold? When life was basically just going through the motions? Did you try to stay free of offense only to realize you were actually deeply wounded? How did you handle it?" Allow a few people to share and then use the responses to help guide the group into the discussion questions.

- **Read:** This week we recommend that you read chapters 13-14 in *The Bait of Satan* book.

- **Devotions:** This week's devotions focus on putting on humility, exercising spiritually, seeking reconciliation, and pursuing peace. Encourage the group once more to invest time daily to read each devotion and answer the questions honestly.

- **Journal:** It is vital for each person to take the truths in this final chapter and make them their own. Ask everyone to listen closely to what the Holy Spirit wants to say and jot down whatever He brings to light during the group discussion, the activity, the video, and the devotions.

GROUP DISCUSSION QUESTIONS

1. What are some of the telltale signs that we're offended? How are our relationships with God and others affected? What do we tend to lose? What indicators of offense have you personally seen in your life?

2. The love we have for others can be healthy or unhealthy—mature or immature. Explain the differences between these two types of love. How does reconciliation fit into the picture?

3. Why do you think people struggle to admit when they're offended? Do you think it's a sign of weakness? Do you believe people feel they're too spiritually mature to be offended?

4. Forgiveness and reconciliation are not the same thing. In your own words, explain the difference between them. Which is the gift from God that must be passed on to others, regardless of their response?

5. Jesus tells us there are two specific situations where we need to *go to our brother or sister* to work through an offense. Describe these situations. Of the two, which seems more difficult to you? Why?

**As a group, consider reading Matthew 5:21-24
and Matthew 18:15-17 (see also Mark 11:25).**

6. In the video teaching, John shares how one of his life-defining moments was his decision to forgive and be reconciled to his mentor. After that he noticed a marked change in every part of his life. He grew as a person and became more productive. What do you think will happen in your life as you choose to forgive and release those who've hurt you? How could your life grow and prosper in ways it hasn't before?

7. A study like *The Bait of Satan* is crucial in helping us be aware of and stay free of offense. How much time and effort would you be willing to invest on a regular basis to keep this topic fresh in your mind (listening to teaching, reading a book, or doing a study)? Do you feel it's important enough to make a part of your schedule? Would you encourage others to do so? If so, why?

ACTIVITY

The crucial step in the forgiveness process that is often forgotten or omitted is to *pray for and bless our enemy*. How can you bless someone who's hurt you? A great way to start is to think of all the ways *you* want to be blessed. Would you like a clean bill of health, solid finances, and strong relationships with family and friends? How about God's protection, wisdom, favor, and close friendship? Pray a blessing on your enemy in these ways. At first, you won't feel like doing it. But when you ask God for His strength, your feelings will begin to line up with your prayers.

In the space below, **write a prayer of blessing** for the one who's hurt you. Pray it out loud once a day for 30 days. During and at the end of the month, *journal* how your heart and attitude change toward that person. This exercise will work wonders in your soul and can be done with anyone who's offended you!

My Prayer of Blessing for

_____

_____

_____

_____

_____

_____

_____

_____

_____

SESSION SUMMARY

○ Pride is a major obstacle to finding freedom from offense.
Admitting when we're offended is not a weakness. It is an act
of humility that positions us to be rescued from the enemy's
trap and restored to a healthy life.

○ While some offenses are less impactful and can be dealt with
quickly, others wound us deeply. Wounds don't heal overnight
and if they're not properly treated, they never heal. The key to
our recovery and protection from further injury is exercising
our spirit.

○ There are certain signs that indicate we've taken the bait and
fallen into the trap of offense. There are also signs that confirm we're being healed from its effects. We need to be wise
enough to recognize these in our lives and the lives of others.

○ God wants us to be reconciled to Him and to our brothers and sisters in Christ. He's given us the gift of reconciliation to reconnect these relationships. Humble repentance is the key to unlock this restoration.

○ To truly walk in agreement with God, we have to surrender our right to be offended. As much as possible, our aim should be to live at peace with everyone.

DAY 1
Dress Yourself in Humility

> *. . . And all of you, dress yourselves in humility*
> *as you relate to one another, for "God opposes*
> *the proud but gives grace to the humble."*
> —1 PETER 5:5 NLT

Pride is a major obstacle to admitting we're offended. It says things like, "I'm tough. I can make it through this. I'm not hurt. I don't need them anyway." Pride keeps us focused and relying on our own strength to handle painful situations instead of trusting in and leaning on God.

According to **Proverbs 11:2; 16:5, 18-19; 21:4; and 1 Peter 5:5,** what does God think of pride? How does He see and respond to us when we're prideful?

_____

_____

_____

If we're full of pride, our confidence is in something other than God. Be honest with yourself: What is your confidence in?

_____

_____

_____

What does God say about trusting in our own ability? Check out **John 6:63; Romans 7:18; Philippians 3:3;** and **John 15:4-5.**

_____

_____

_____

_____

_____

Humility is the antidote for pride. How does God feel about it, and how will He bless us when we stay humble? Read **Proverbs 15:33; 22:4; James 4:6-10; Matthew 18:2-4; 23:11-12;** and **Psalm 37:11; 149:4,** and write what the Lord shows you about this amazing, God-honoring quality.

_____

_____

_____

_____

"Believer, study the humility of Jesus! This is the secret, the hidden root of your redemption. Sink down into it deeper day by day. Believe with your whole heart that this Christ, Whom God has given you, even as His divine humility accomplished the work for you, will enter in to dwell and work within you too . . . It is only by the indwelling of Christ in His divine humility that we become truly humble."—ANDREW MURRAY[1]

Where does humility come from? Spending time with Jesus and allowing Him to impart His Spirit into our lives moment by moment. Meditate on the examples in **Matthew 11:28-30; John 13:1-17;** and **Philippians 2:1-8,** then write what God speaks to you.

_____

_____

_____

_____

_____

DAY 2
Exercise Your Soul and Spirit

. . . I exercise myself, to have always a conscience
void of offense toward God, and toward men.
—ACTS 24:16 KJV

Jesus said in Luke 17:1 that it is impossible for offenses not to come. Therefore, if we're going to live free of offense, it's going to take effort—effort Paul compares to *exercise*. While few like to talk about exercise, much less do it, it has the power to keep us healthy—body, soul, and spirit.

All exercise provides specific benefits, whether it's traditional sports, aerobics, swimming, or weight training. What rewards and advantages have you gained from exercise?

_____

_____

_____

_____

What kind of benefits do you think come from exercising spiritually to steer clear of the trap of offense?

_____

_____

_____

EXERCISE: Exertion made for the sake of *training* or physical fitness [or spiritual fitness]; a task or problem done or practiced to develop skill.[2] The Greek work for *exercise* in Acts 24:16 is *askeo*—a word which generally signifies "to take pains, endeavor, exercise by training or discipline."[3]

[Words in brackets added for clarity;
italics added for emphasis.]

Just as there are certain ways to build strength physically, there are specific "exercises" we can do to build spiritual strength. Think for a minute: What activities build your faith? What breaks down barriers between you and God and fills you with His love, joy, peace, and hope? What difference do you feel overall when these happen regularly?

_____

_____

_____

_____

_____

_____

Consider these time-tested strength builders: Isaiah 40:29-31; Psalm 27:13-14; John 15:1-8; 2 Timothy 3:16-17; Psalm 119:165; Proverbs 27:17; Hebrews 10:24-25; Exodus 15:1-2; Ephesians 6:10-18; 1 Corinthians 14:4; and Jude 1:20.

Now that you know what brings you close to God and strengthens you, how can you begin to make room for these practices in your schedule? What may need to change in your life to allow your faith to grow? Take a moment with Jesus and ask Him to show you. Together, write out a plan to create more opportunities to get closer.

_____

_____

_____

_____

_____

Exercise daily in God—no spiritual flabbiness, please! Workouts in the gymnasium are useful, but a disciplined life in God is far more so, making you fit both today and forever. You can count on this . . . .—1 TIMOTHY 4:7-9 MSG

DAY 3
Check Your Vital Signs

> *Examine and test and evaluate your own selves*
> *to see whether you are holding to your faith*
> *and showing the proper fruits of it . . . .*
> —2 CORINTHIANS 13:5 AMP

If you're on the road to recovery from the effects of offense, there will be signs to confirm it. One of the greatest indicators that you're being healed is greater health in your relationship with God. There is no true healing apart from abiding in Him.

Seasoned author, counselor, and teacher John Eldredge states:

> "There are no formulas with God. The way in which God
> heals our wound is a deeply personal process. He is a person
> and He insists on working personally. For some, it comes
> in a moment of divine touch. For others, it takes place over
> time and through the help of another, maybe several others.
> . . . Healing never happens outside of intimacy with Christ.
> The healing of our wound flows out of our union with
> Him."[4]

How would you describe your relationship with God? Is it thriving, barely surviving, or somewhere in between? How does your relationship now compare with what it was a year or two ago? When was the last time you truly felt God's presence? What do your answers say to you?

_____

_____

_____

_____

On a scale of 1 to 10, rate the following (1 being *absolutely not* or *never*, 10 being *always*):

____ I enjoy reading God's Word.

____ I love listening to and talking with God in prayer.

____ I'm excited about going to church.

____ I enjoy serving others (in the community/at church).

____ I believe God loves me deeply.

____ I trust God to handle the difficult people in my life.

____ I look forward to getting up each day to see what adventure God takes me on.

The highest score is 70, and 7 would be the lowest. Do you like what you scored? In what areas could you improve? Does your score reveal anything alarming? The good news is, regardless of your score, you can improve upon it as you grow in relationship with Jesus.

_____

_____

_____

Another sign that God is healing your wounded heart is a positive change in how you feel toward the one who hurt you. Be honest: Are you sincerely or half-heartedly praying for your offender?

_____

_____

_____

_____

If you've been praying, have your attitude, thoughts, and/or feelings changed since you began? Has the initial sting subsided?

_____

_____

_____

_____

Stop and think: What is it that causes you to come to God and repent? When did He forgive you? When were you reconciled (brought back into right relationship) with Him? What do these answers say to you about forgiving your enemy and being reconciled to him or her?

_____

_____

_____

_____

Consider Romans 2:4; 5:8; and Luke 23:33-34.

DAY 4
Seek Reconciliation

We are Christ's ambassadors. God is using us to speak to you:
we beg you, as though Christ Himself were here pleading with
you, receive the love He offers you—be reconciled to God.

—2 CORINTHIANS 5:20 TLB

Once you have forgiven the person who hurt you—and you know you're healed—it's time to seek to make things right with them. God calls this *reconciliation*.

In their book *Boundaries*, Dr. Henry Cloud and Dr. John Townsend stated:

"The Bible is clear about two principles: (1) We always need to forgive, but (2) we don't always achieve reconciliation. *Forgiveness* is something that we do in our hearts; we release someone from a debt that they owe us. We write off the person's debt, and she no longer owes us. We no longer condemn her. She is clean. Only *one* party is needed for forgiveness: *me*. The person who owes me a debt does not have to ask my forgiveness. It is a work of grace in my heart.

This brings us to the second principle: We do not always achieve reconciliation. God forgave the world, but the *whole* world is not reconciled to Him. Although He may have forgiven all people, all people have not owned their sin and appropriated His forgiveness. That would be *reconciliation*. Forgiveness takes one; reconciliation takes *two*."[5]

In light of Dr. Cloud and Dr. Townsend's quote, has God asked you to go to the person who hurt you and apologize? If He has, have you done it? If you haven't, what is holding you back?

_____

_____

_____

_____

Imagine: You've had a disagreement with another believer—we'll call him Bill—who's still upset and constantly avoiding you. One day as you're praying, God prompts you to go and be reconciled to him. How would you handle this? Briefly explain your *attitudes* and *actions*— what would you do and what would you *not* do?

_____

_____

_____

_____

Using the situation with Bill, imagine that you go to him with the right attitude and try to make things right, but he refuses to listen. How should you handle it? (Check out **Matthew 18:16-17.**)

_____

_____

_____

It's the kindness of God that softens our hearts and leads us to make things right with Him. Similarly, when we show kindness to someone who has mistreated us, we set the stage for reconciliation. What practical steps can you take to create an atmosphere filled with God's love?

_____

_____

_____

_____

_____

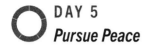

DAY 5
Pursue Peace

> *Pursue peace with all people, and holiness,*
> *without which no one will see the Lord.*
> —Hebrews 12:14

While it *is* God's will that we be reconciled to each other, it will not always be attainable. That's why He tells us in Romans 12:18, "If it is possible, *as much as depends on you,* live peaceably with all men." As we do our best to mend broken relationships, He will honor our efforts. Take a few moments to meditate on these passages:

> So let's agree to use all our energy in getting along with each other. Help others with encouraging words; don't drag them down by finding fault.—Romans 14:19 msg

> For let him who wants to enjoy life and see good days [good—whether apparent or not] keep his tongue free from evil and his lips from guile (treachery, deceit). Let him turn away from wickedness and shun it, and let him do right. Let him search for peace (harmony; undisturbedness from fears, agitating passions, and moral conflicts) and seek it eagerly. [Do not merely desire peaceful relations with God, with your fellowmen, and with yourself, but pursue, go after them!]—1 Peter 3:10-11 amp

> But the wisdom that comes from heaven is first of all pure and full of quiet gentleness. Then it is peace-loving and courteous.

It allows discussion and is willing to yield to others; it is full of mercy and good deeds. It is wholehearted and straightforward and sincere. And those who are peacemakers will plant seeds of peace and reap a harvest of goodness.—JAMES 3:17-18 TLB

And let the peace (soul harmony which comes) from Christ rule (act as umpire continually) in your hearts [deciding and settling with finality all questions that arise in your minds, in that peaceful state] to which as [members of Christ's] one body you were also called [to live] . . . .—COLOSSIANS 3:15 AMP

What is God speaking to you about peace in these verses? Why is it so important to pursue?

_____

_____

_____

_____

When someone tries to make peace with you, what words and/or attitudes *close* your heart and which ones *open* your heart? How does this guide your efforts?

_____

_____

_____

_____

Another powerful way to make peace with someone is to give them a gift. A peace offering, as some call it, has an amazing ability to lower walls of defense and open a heart. Get quiet and ask God to show you just the right gift for the one who hurt you and the best time to give it. Pray for His blessing on the giving and receiving of the gift. Write out the plan of action He gives you.

_____

_____

_____

_____

_____

_____

_____

_____

"A quietly given gift soothes an irritable person; a heartfelt present cools a hot temper."—PROVERBS 21:14 MSG

PRAYER OF FORGIVENESS
"Father, thank You for speaking to me through this study.
I realize that I've sinned against You by harboring unfor-
giveness and offense. I also realize that two wrongs don't
make things right. I've justified my sin far too long because
of how badly I was treated. So at this moment, I come to

Your throne and ask You to forgive me for unforgiveness, bitterness, resentment, and harboring this offense. I repent of this right now, and surrender this person and situation into Your hands. Right now, from my heart, I choose to forgive _____. [Say each person's name who hurt you—releasing them individually. See them in your mind and say to them, 'I forgive you and I release you. You owe me nothing.'] *In the merciful and precious name of Jesus, Amen."*

Date: _____

Now *exercise daily* by praying for this person, speaking God's blessings over their life. Refer back to this chapter's activity for how and what to pray for them.

FOOD FOR THOUGHT . . .

Jesus forgave us long before we were reconciled to Him. He wants to empower us to be reconciled with not only Him, but others who've offended us. Our sin of staying offended is not justified by the way we were mistreated—God has far greater plans for us than that! His mature love in us covers a mountain of sin, always hopes for restoration, and heals us from the inside out.

Seize this moment with Jesus to think of past, severed relationships that need reconciliation. Are you willing to do what it takes to reach peace? Sit with God for a few minutes. Ask Him for the wisdom to know how and with whom to pursue restoration. Pour your heart out on paper, capturing the insight He gives you.

_____

_____

_____

_____

_____

_____

_____

_____

_____

_____

_____

_____

_____

(1) Andrew Murray, *Humility* (Fort Washington, PA: CLC Publications, 1997) pp. 23, 42.
(2) Adapted from *Merriam-Webster's Desk Dictionary* (Springfield, MA: Merriam-Webster, Incorporated, 1995). (3) Adapted from *Vine's Complete Expository Dictionary of Old and New Testament Words,* W.E. Vine (Nashville, TN: Thomas Nelson Publishing, 1996). (4) John Eldredge, *Wild at Heart* (Nashville, TN: Thomas Nelson Publishers, 2001) pp. 127-128. (5) Dr. Henry Cloud, Dr. John Townsend, *Boundaries* (Grand Rapids, MI: Zondervan Publishing House, 1992) p. 251.

How to Receive Salvation

If you confess with your mouth that Jesus is Lord and believe in your heart that God raised Him from the dead, you will be saved. For it is by believing in your heart that you are made right with God, and it is by confessing with your mouth that you are saved.
—ROMANS 10:9–10 NLT

God wants to see you positioned for eternal success. He's passionate about you and the plan He has for your life. But there's only one way to start the journey to your destiny: by receiving salvation through God's Son, Jesus Christ.

Through the death and resurrection of Jesus, God has made the way for you to enter His kingdom as a beloved son or daughter. The sacrifice of Jesus on the cross made eternal and abundant life freely available to you. Salvation is God's gift to you; you cannot do anything to earn or deserve it.

To receive this precious gift, first acknowledge your sin of living independently of your Creator (for this is the root of all the sins you have committed). This repentance is a vital part of receiving salvation. Peter made this clear on the day that five thousand were saved in the book of Acts: "Repent therefore and be converted, that your sins may be blotted out" (Acts 3:19). Scripture declares that each of us is born a slave to sin. This slavery is rooted in the sin of Adam, who began the pattern of willful disobedience. Repentance is a choice to walk away from obedience to yourself and Satan, the father of lies, and to turn in obedience to your new Master, Jesus Christ—the One who gave His life for you.

You must give Jesus lordship over your life. To make Jesus "Lord" means you give Him ownership of your life (spirit, soul, and body)—everything you are and have. His authority over your life becomes absolute. The moment you do this, God delivers you from darkness and transfers you to the light and glory of His kingdom. You simply go from death to life—you become His child!

If you want to receive salvation through Jesus, pray these words:

God in Heaven, I acknowledge that I am a sinner and have fallen short of Your righteous standard. I deserve to be judged for eternity for my sin. Thank You for not leaving me in this state, for I believe You sent Jesus Christ, Your only begotten Son, who was born of the virgin Mary, to die for me and carry my judgment on the cross. I believe He was raised again on the third day and is now seated at Your right hand as my Lord and Savior. So on this day, I repent of my independence from You and give my life entirely to the lordship of Jesus.

Jesus, I confess you as my Lord and Savior. Come into my life through Your Spirit and change me into a child of God. I renounce the things of darkness which I once held onto, and from this day forward I will no longer live for myself. By Your grace, I will live for You who gave Yourself for me that I may live forever.

Thank You, Lord. My life is now completely in Your hands, and according to Your Word, I shall never be ashamed.

Welcome to the family of God! I encourage you to share your exciting news with another believer. It's also important that you join a Bible-believing local church and connect with others who can encourage you in your new faith.

You have just embarked on the most remarkable journey. May you grow in revelation, grace, and friendship with God every day!

Introducing
MessengerX

Now you can access our entire library of discipleship content! Download the app at no cost today.

Scan the QR code to download MessengerX

MessengerX.com

BOOKS BY JOHN

Messenger International exists to develop
uncompromising followers of Christ who
transform our world.

Call: 1-800-648-1477

Visit us online at: MessengerInternational.org

Connect with John Bevere:

JohnBevere.com